Learning Styles Questionnaire
40-item version
Peter Honey

To find out more about learning and learning styles visit our website:

www.peterhoney.com

ISBN-13: 978-1-902899-27-5

ISBN-10: 1-902899-27-X

Published by Peter Honey Publications Limited

First edition published January 2006

First reprint July 2007, second reprint November 2008

Peter Honey Publications Limited

Registered Office: 10 Linden Avenue Maidenhead Berks SL6 6HB

Tel: +44 (0)1628 633 946 Fax: +44 (0)1628 633 262 Email: info@peterhoney.com

Website: www.peterhoney.com

VAT No. GB208066480   Registered in England and Wales No. 3754757

CONTENTS

Foreword

The Honey & Mumford Learning Styles Questionnaire (80-item version) was first published in the autumn of 1982. Since then it has been widely used throughout the world, in all sectors of commerce and education, to help people identify and benefit from their learning style preferences.

In the intervening years, the process of learning, 'learning to learn' and lifelong learning has attracted growing interest and been increasingly recognised as a key (perhaps even *the* key) life skill. Being aware of your learning style preferences is now widely acknowledged as a prerequisite to becoming a more effective learner.

In 2000 we produced a shorter, online version of the questionnaire as an integral part of our *Learning Series.* The 40-item version is better suited to the online technology (all our online development tools are approximately 40 items in length) and it has proved popular with users. In the light of this development, it seems sensible to make the shorter version of the questionnaire available to an even wider audience – hence this booklet. The rationale for a shorter version of the questionnaire, and how it compares with the 80-item version, is expanded upon in the Appendix.

This booklet will help you to identify your preferred styles and optimise your learning effectiveness by guiding you towards learning opportunities that will best suit your preferences. It will also help you to learn more easily from a greater variety of learning opportunities by showing you how to expand your repertoire and become proficient at all four stages of the learning cycle: experiencing, reviewing, concluding and planning. You will also find valuable advice about the sort of help you can expect from your manager - given that he/she also has learning style preferences!

Everything you need is in this booklet. As Aldous Huxley said, 'The great end of learning is not knowledge, but action.' Go for it!

Peter Honey

SECTION 1

An introduction to learning – your most important capability

You are a product of your learning. Everything you know, everything you can do and everything you believe, you have learnt.

Despite your learning being largely responsible for who you are (you are what you learn!) it is probably something you tend to take for granted. Once we have left formal education, we continue to learn every day without necessarily realising it.

Learning is your most important capability simply because it is the gateway to every other capability you might wish to develop. Whether you want to become fluent in another language, and/or become better at winning friends and influencing people, and/or become better at surfing the web, and/or better at football, learning is the key. The process of learning underpins *everything*.

Another striking thing about the learning process is that it is impossible to imagine it will ever become obsolete. Human beings will always need to learn to develop their skills and adapt to changing circumstances. *What* we learn may become obsolete, but *how* we learn will always remain a priority.

What is learning?

The answer to this question depends on whether you are focusing on learning as an internal process, i.e. where information taken in by your senses is processed by your brain, or whether you are thinking of learning as a series of external inputs and outputs. The workings of the brain are so complex that neuroscientists are not yet able to give a complete answer to the question, 'what is learning?'.

External inputs and outputs are far easier to track than the internal goings-on that forge connections between the two. Certainly, the outputs of learning are relatively easy to recognise – you can demonstrate that you know and/or can do something that you didn't know and/or couldn't do before you had learned.

But concentrating on the outputs alone makes learning sound as if it is a boring mechanistic process. Nothing could be further from the truth. The scope of learning, and understanding what is involved in getting better at it, makes learning endlessly fascinating and intriguing.

The following list of characteristics (not in any order of importance) may help to whet your appetite.

1 **Learning is both a process and an outcome**

We use the same word to describe the 'hows' of learning ('I did a search on the web')
and the 'whats' of learning ('I found out about the planets').

2 **Learning is both formal and informal**

We can learn by participating in a formal learning event such as a course or
conference and we can learn from our everyday experiences, e.g. a chat over lunch
with a colleague.

3 **Learning is both conscious and unconscious**

We can learn deliberately and describe what and how we learned (explicit learning)
and we can learn automatically, by a process of osmosis, without realising it (tacit
learning).

4 **Learning is both nice and nasty**

We can have fun learning and find it a thoroughly enjoyable process and we can find it
tough-going and frustrating.

5 **Learning is both planned and accidental**

We can identify our learning needs and plan how to meet them and we can learn from
unplanned events that happened by chance (life's rich tapestry).

6 **Learning is both desirable and undesirable**

We can learn things that are useful and beneficial (good habits) and we can learn
things that are inappropriate and/or harmful (bad habits).

7 **Learning is both incremental and transformational**

We can learn gradually by taking little steps and we can learn by having a 'Road to
Damascus' experience that transforms us.

8 **Learning is both a social and a solitary activity**

We can learn collaboratively with and from other people and we can learn on our own
through, for example, studying and reflection.

9 **Learning is both reactive and proactive**

We can learn after an experience (with the benefit of hindsight) and we can learn by
having a premeditated need or objective and a plan to achieve it.

10 **Learning is both about acquiring knowledge and acquiring skills**

We can learn so that we add to our store of knowledge and insights and we can learn
to develop our skills and talents.

---

11 Learning is both voluntary and compulsory

We can learn because we want to and we can learn because we are required to.

12 Learning is both recognised and unrecognised

We can be rewarded and/or receive accreditation for our learning and we can do it for its own sake, with no acknowledgement or recognition.

13 Learning is both supported and unsupported

We can get lots of encouragement and support whilst learning and we can be left to get on with it as best we can.

14 Learning is both shared and private

We can share our learning with others and we can choose to keep it to ourselves.

15 Learning is both superficial and deep

We can learn by rote without real understanding and we can learn by thoroughly internalising the principles.

16 Learning is both active and passive

We can learn by having a go and experimenting and we can learn by listening, watching and reading.

17 Learning is both taught and self-managed

We can learn from opportunities that are provided by other people (their agenda) and we can take full responsibility for our own learning (our agenda).

18 Learning is both short-term and long-term

We can indulge in some just-in-time, quick-fix learning and we can invest in our development over a lifetime.

Hopefully this list of characteristics will open your eyes to the sheer scope of learning and excite rather than depress you! Learning is the key to your continued effectiveness and to leading an interesting, fulfilled life.

The challenge is to treat your learning as a skill that, like all your other skills, needs to be consciously reviewed and developed.

SECTION 2

An introduction to learning style preferences

We all have preferences – places we prefer, people we prefer and activities we prefer. It is interesting to ponder where your preferences came from. They might be so ingrained, such an integral part of who you are, that you assume they are inherited, rather like your physical characteristics and your blood group.

An alternative view is that your preferences gradually emerged from thousands of experiences that you unconsciously sorted into those you liked and those you didn't like. If your preferences have been acquired (making them, literally, an acquired taste!) it means that they are malleable, not inherited or fixed like your blood group. This in turn means that your preferences can alter over time as you adapt to new experiences. For example, you might have a job that requires you to pay careful attention to detail and to be risk-averse. If you then switched to a job that required you to keep the big picture in mind and take calculated risks, the chances are that your preferences would slowly adapt to mesh with your new situation.

The view taken in this booklet is that preferences have themselves been learned and can therefore change over time – either because you want them to or because of changed circumstances. This opens up the possibility of strengthening under-utilised learning style preferences so that you can learn more easily from a greater range of learning opportunities.

The learning cycle helps us to understand why an expanded repertoire might be beneficial.

The Learning Cycle

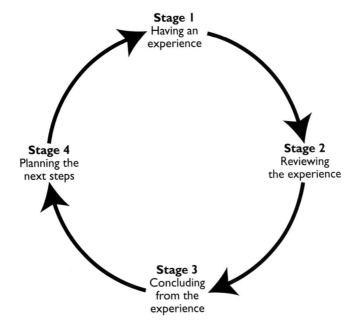

Stage 1: Having an experience

There are two different ways to have an experience. One is to let the experience come to you (reactive) and the other is to seek it out deliberately (proactive). The opportunities to learn are greatly increased if the normal everyday things that happen to us are supplemented by extra experiences we create. Suppose, for example, you regularly attend a weekly meeting that tends to be deadly dull. You could decide to view it as a learning opportunity and start to experiment with different ways of livening up the meeting.

Stage 2: Reviewing the experience

If you are to learn from an experience it is vital to review what happened during it. In the deadly dull meeting, for example, you might experiment by having a different person take the chair for different agenda items. Your review might then focus on the differences you observed between the way the best and the worst chairperson undertook the task.

Stage 3: Concluding from the experience

Concluding involves scanning the raw material from the review for conclusions, 'answers' or lessons learned. It helps if the conclusions are specific rather than global. After the meeting you might conclude that the best chairperson:

- clarified the objective of whatever was to be discussed

- actively sought people's ideas

- summarised at frequent intervals.

Stage 4: Planning the next steps

Planning involves translating some of the conclusions into a form in which they can be actioned. An example might be to spend ten minutes at the start of the next meeting discussing your conclusions about the best chairperson and working out how to help those who had most difficulty with the three modes of behaviour.

Learning as a continuous process

The four stages in the process of learning from experience are mutually dependent on one another. No stage makes sense, or is particularly useful, in isolation from the others.

You can start anywhere on the cycle because each stage feeds into the next. A person could, for example, start at stage 2 by acquiring some information and pondering it before reaching some conclusions at stage 3, and deciding how to apply it at stage 4. On the other hand, someone could start at stage 4 with a technique that they plan to incorporate into their working methods. Using the technique would then be stage 1 in the cycle, reviewing how it worked out, stage 2, reaching conclusions, stage 3, and modifying the technique in the light of the experience, stage 4.

This continuous, iterative process is so fundamental that it underpins many other approaches. The scientific method is one example. Many problem-solving/decision-making processes also map onto the stages in the learning cycle.

Ways of distorting the learning cycle

The four stages - experiencing, reviewing, concluding and planning - are mutually supportive. None is fully effective as a learning procedure on its own. Each stage plays an equally important part in the total process (though the time spent on each may vary considerably).

Most people, however, develop preferences that give them a liking for certain stages over others. The preferences lead to a distortion of the learning process so that greater emphasis is placed on some stages to the detriment of others. Here are some typical examples:

Distortion 1

Preferences for experiencing to the extent that people develop an addiction for activities and cannot sit still. They have to be rushing around constantly on the go. This results in plenty of experiences and the assumption that having experiences is synonymous with learning from them.

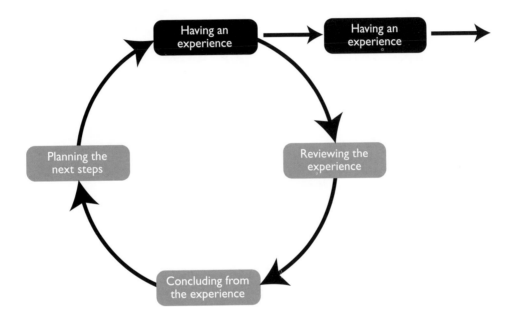

Distortion 2

Preferences for reviewing such that people shy away from first-hand experiences and postpone reaching conclusions for as long as possible or, more accurately, reach the conclusion that more information is required! This results in an 'analysis to paralysis' tendency with plenty of pondering but little action.

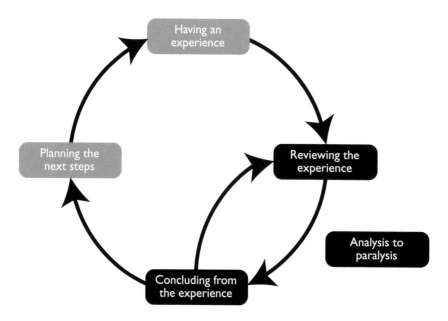

Distortion 3

Preferences for seizing on an expedient course of action and implementing it with inadequate analysis. This results in a tendency to go for 'quick fixes' by overemphasising the planning and experiencing stages to the detriment of reviewing and concluding.

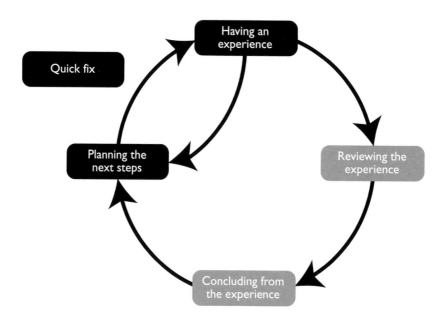

Distortion 4

Preferences for concluding such that people have a compulsion to reach an answer quickly. This results in a tendency to jump to conclusions by circumventing the review stage, where uncertainty and ambiguity are higher. (Conclusions, even if they are the wrong ones, are comforting things to have.)

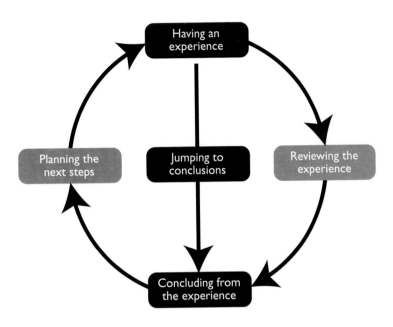

Arguably, the 'best' learners are equally comfortable with *all* the stages in the learning cycle. However, as we shall see, all-rounders are rare. Most people have learning style preferences that make some stages in the cycle seem more attractive than others. Unless they intervene to correct this, by, for example, deliberately investing more energy in the parts of the learning cycle they feel least comfortable with, they are likely to succumb to one or other of the distortions discussed above.

The overriding point to remember is that each stage in the learning cycle is a 25% contributor to the whole. Section 9 goes into more detail about how you can set about strengthening an under-utilised style.

SECTION 3

The Learning Jigsaw – putting learning styles into perspective

This booklet focuses on your learning style preferences and helps you to see how an awareness of your preferences can help you to become a more effective learner. Understanding your learning style is a good place to start, but you should appreciate that learning styles are only one piece in the learning jigsaw.

The essence of effective learning is that it:

- sticks for as long as it needs to

- gets used appropriately

- makes a difference for the better.

There are many factors that influence the effectiveness of both the processes and the outcomes of learning. Broadly, they fall into four groupings:

- you, the learner

- your situation/circumstances

- the nature of the learning subject matter

- the methods employed.

Here are some examples of the various factors that typically impinge on the efficiency of your learning.

Factors about you, the learner

- Your preferred learning style(s)

- Whether your previous personal experiences of learning were favourable or unfavourable

- Your motivation, i.e. how eager you are to learn

- Your learning skills and techniques, i.e. the extent to which you are equipped to self-manage your learning

- Your familiarity with the subject matter

- Whether you see the learning as relevant and beneficial

Factors about your situation/circumstances

- The extent to which your learning is actively encouraged and supported

- Whether the learning is a 'requirement' or being undertaken voluntarily

- The extent to which there are plentiful opportunities to use/apply your learning

- Whether your learning needs have been identified accurately – and by whom

- How your learning is to be assessed

- Whether the learning is urgent (just-in-time)

- Whether you are expected to learn in your own time or at work

- The ease with which the learning can be accessed

- Whether the physical environment is conducive to learning (lighting, temperature, low noise level, etc.)

Factors about the subject matter

- Whether the learning is primarily aimed at increasing your knowledge, or developing your skills and/or modifying your attitudes

- Whether the learning is broken down into manageable chunks appropriate to your skills and experience

- The extent to which you find the subject matter comprehensible/meaningful

- Whether you are required to learn by rote (surface learning) or with full understanding (deep learning)

- Whether the content lends itself to logical, sequential treatment or inspirational, emotional treatment

Factors about the methods employed

- The appropriateness of the delivery mechanism – human or otherwise

- The extent to which you find the learning method(s) helpful/engaging

- The extent to which the learning is structured

- The extent to which your learning is supported and reinforced

- Whether the methods require you to learn by yourself or with others

- The extent to which the method(s) are passive or active

- Whether the methods provide you with timely feedback

A long list - and there are more factors where these come from! So, please do not assume that knowledge of learning styles alone is all there is to becoming a more effective learner. Learning styles are certainly an important factor – but only one piece in the jigsaw puzzle.

In summary: why it is worth knowing about your learning style preferences?

One size doesn't fit all

People vary. They come in different shapes and sizes and have different personalities and likes and dislikes. They also develop preferences about how they like to learn.

This is a deep-seated preference that is rarely discussed, mainly because people go about their lives without thinking much about learning. In fact, if you conducted a poll and asked people a question such as, 'How do you prefer to learn?', the chances are you'd get a lot of blank faces.

The 'L' question is a tough one to answer because, after leaving formal education, most people tend to take learning for granted; they just do it in parallel with all the other things life's rich tapestry throws at them. It is rather like breathing – a vital process for survival that is largely left to its own devices (until, that is, you have breathing problems and then it zooms to the top of the agenda!).

Learning is a learnable skill

Learning is a precious capability and it is much safer to assume that learning is a skill that is deserving of some tender loving care. Like any other skill, it can be studied, understood, practised, experimented with, honed and polished and continuously improved.

Learning styles provide a brilliant starting point. Once you have a snapshot (that's all it is!) of your learning style preferences, you are in a better position to make some important choices. You could, for example, choose to play to your strengths and use the information about yourself to decide which learning methods suit you and which do not. This reduces the inefficient, hit-and-miss business of exposing yourself to all sorts of experiences that, quite literally, 'aren't your style'. You could also choose to expand your repertoire by deciding to strengthen an under-utilised style.

Learning Styles and the 'Aha' experience

Knowing your learning style preferences can be a revelation. Suddenly things fall into place. 'Now I know why I hated that course', 'So that's why I'd rather assemble flat-pack furniture before reading the instructions', 'No wonder I couldn't get on with my last boss – our learning style preferences didn't mesh', 'Now I know why I get irritated when people talk while I'm still reading'.

Learning Styles - a place of embarkation, not a destination

Tempting though it is, knowledge of your learning style preferences must never be used as an excuse to stay the way you are. Learning style preferences are malleable, not fixed. The whole idea is to use the information as a platform to become a more effective learner. The questionnaire in this booklet is designed to provide you with a helpful starting point.

SECTION 4

The 40-item Learning Styles Questionnaire

This short questionnaire will help you discover your learning style preferences. We all develop learning 'habits' that make us happier to learn in some ways and less happy to learn in other, less familiar, ways. Most people are only vaguely aware of their learning preferences. This questionnaire will clarify your preferred ways of learning so that you are in a better position to select experiences that suit your style and/or to broaden your scope by strengthening under-utilised styles.

There is no time limit for the completion of this questionnaire. It will probably take you 5 to 10 minutes. The accuracy of the results depends on how honest you are. There are no right or wrong answers. If you agree more than you disagree with a statement put a tick (✓) in the box. If you disagree more than you agree with a statement put a cross (✗) in the box. Be sure to mark each item with either a tick or a cross.

1. I quite like taking risks.

2. Before taking part in a discussion or meeting, I like to read the appropriate papers and prepare carefully.

3. I like to be absolutely correct about things.

4. I like practical, tried and tested techniques.

5. I often do things just because I feel like it, rather than thinking about them first.

6. I make decisions only after weighing up the pros and cons of different possibilities.

7. I prefer to solve problems using a systematic approach that reduces guesswork and uncertainty.

8. What matters most is whether something works in practice.

9. I actively look for new things to do.

10   I prefer to establish the facts and think things through before reaching a conclusion.

11   I like to check things out for myself rather than take them for granted.

12   When I hear about a new idea or technique, I immediately start working out how to apply it to my situation/problems.

13   I like the challenge of trying out different ways of doing things.

14   I prefer to have as many bits of information about a subject as possible. The more I have to sift through the better.

15   I am quite keen on sticking to fixed routines, following procedures and keeping to timetables.

16   In discussions, I like to get straight to the point.

17   I prefer to jump in and do things as they come along rather than plan things out beforehand.

18   I prefer to base decisions on hard evidence and not to trust a hunch or intuition.

19   I like to fit things into some sort of pattern, framework or model.

20   I tend to judge people's ideas on their practical merits.

21   In discussions, I usually come up with lots of spontaneous ideas.

22   I prefer to look at a problem from as many different angles as I can before starting to solve it.

23   I prefer to evaluate the soundness of my ideas before sharing them.

24   In meetings and discussions, I put forward ideas that I know are down-to-earth and realistic.

25   Usually I talk more than I listen.

26   If I have to write a report or a formal letter, I prefer to have several rough drafts before settling on the final version.

27   I am rather fussy about how I do things – a bit of a perfectionist.

28   I find that I can often work out more practical ways of doing things.

29   I find rules and procedures take the fun out of things.

30   I like to consider many options before I make up my mind.

31   I believe that careful, logical thinking is the key to success.

32   I prefer ideas with an obvious relevance to my life and work.

33   I'm usually the 'life and soul' of the party.

34   I like to think through the consequences before taking action.

35   I like to understand the assumptions, principles and rationale upon which things are based.

36   In my opinion, it doesn't matter how you do something, as long as it works.

37   I enjoy the excitement of a crisis situation.

38   I usually do more listening than talking.

39   I like meetings and discussions to be structured and orderly.

40   I do whatever I need to, to get the job done.

SECTION 5

Learning style descriptions

Activists

Activists like to take direct action. They are enthusiastic and welcome new challenges and experiences. They are less interested in what has happened in the past or in putting things into a broader context. They are primarily interested in the here and now. They like to have a go, try things out and participate. They like to be the centre of attention.

So, in summary, Activists like:

- to think on their feet
- to have short sessions
- plenty of variety
- the opportunity to initiate
- to participate and have fun.

Reflectors

Reflectors like to think about things in detail before taking action. They take a thoughtful approach. They are good listeners and prefer to adopt a low profile. They are prepared to read and re-read and will welcome the opportunity to repeat a piece of learning.

So, in summary, Reflectors like:

- to think before acting
- thorough preparation
- to research and evaluate
- to make decisions in their own time
- to listen and observe.

Theorists

Theorists like to see how things fit into an overall pattern. They are logical and objective systems people who prefer a sequential approach to problems. They are analytical, pay great attention to detail and tend to be perfectionists.

So, in summary, Theorists like:

- concepts and models
- to see the overall picture
- to feel intellectually stretched
- structure and clear objectives
- logical presentation of ideas.

Pragmatists

Pragmatists like to see how things work in practice. They enjoy experimenting with new ideas. They are practical, down to earth and like to solve problems. They appreciate the opportunity to try out what they have learned/are learning.

So, in summary, Pragmatists like:

- to see the relevance of their work
- to gain practical advantage from learning
- credible role models
- proven techniques
- activities to be real.

SECTION 6

Score Key

You score one point for each item ticked (✓). There are no points for items you crossed (✗).

You will find a score key attached to the back cover of this booklet. This is designed to make it easy to transfer your scores from the questionnaire on pages 14 - 16.

Simply fold out the score key and record your responses in the boxes provided.

Then plot your scores on the profile chart on page 21 to get a relative feel for the strength of your preferences.

SECTION 7

Understanding your results

Having scored your questionnaire, you will now have four scores ranging from 0 - 10 for Activist, Reflector, Theorist and Pragmatist. Obviously, your highest score (or scores if you have some that tie) indicates your strongest learning style preference with other preferences lagging behind.

You might, however, like to compare your scores with those achieved by over 13,000 other people. The table below gives 'norms' that divide the scores into five categories:

The top 10% of scores – very strong preferences

The next 20% of scores – strong preferences

The middle 40% of score – moderate preferences

The next 20% of scores – low preferences

The bottom 10% of scores – very low preferences

Simply, locate and ring your four scores on the table on the following page so that you can see at a glance which band they fall into. You'll see that the weightings are slightly different. For example, a score of 8 for Activist is in the strong preference band whereas the same score for the other three styles is in the moderate band. On balance, it is safer to interpret your result by taking the norms into account – especially when they are based on such a large population.

Activist	Reflector	Theorist	Pragmatist	
10	10	10	10	Very Strong
9				Preference
8				Strong
7				Preference
6	9	9	9	Moderate
		8		Preference
5	8	7	8	
4	7	6	7	Low
	6			Preference
3	5	5	6	
2	4	4	5	
	3	3	4	
1	2	2	3	Very Low
	1	1	2	Preference
			1	
0	0	0	0	

SECTION 8

How to choose learning activities to suit your learning style

Different learning activities tend to be more compatible with certain learning style preferences. Where individual preferences and activities match, learning is more likely. If there is a mismatch you are less likely to learn and/or will find learning more of a struggle.

This section will show you how you can choose activities that are likely to dovetail with your style. We also indicate the activities it may pay you to avoid, unless you are given special help in coping with them.

Here are four checklists to guide you towards learning activities that suit your style. You do not have to study the detail on all of them. Just concentrate on the parts that are relevant to you in the light of your Learning Styles Questionnaire result.

We hope these checklists will guide you towards suitable learning experiences. The checklists will also help you identify the kind of work experiences from which you are most likely to learn and benefit.

These checklists are followed by some key questions that you should ask before engaging in any learning activity. Whenever the answer to some (or all) the questions in each batch is 'no', the activity is not a good fit with your preferred learning style.

If you have a preference for the **Activist** style:

you will learn most easily from activities where

- there are **new** experiences/problems/ opportunities from which to learn
- you can engross yourself in short 'here and now' activities
- there is excitement/drama/crisis
- things chop and change and there are diverse activities to tackle
- you have a lot of the limelight
- you are allowed to generate lots of ideas
- you are thrown in at the deep end with a task you think is difficult/challenging
- you are involved with other people, e.g. bouncing ideas off them, solving problems as part of a team
- it is appropriate to 'have a go'.

you will find it more difficult to learn from activities where

- learning involves a passive role, e.g. listening to lectures, monologues, explanations, statements of how things should be done, reading, watching
- you are asked to stand back and not be involved
- you are required to engage in solitary work, i.e. reading, writing or thinking on your own
- you are asked to repeat essentially the same activity over and over again, e.g. when practising
- you have precise instructions to follow with little room for manoeuvre
- you are asked to do a thorough job, e.g. attend to detail, tie up loose ends, dot i's and cross t's.

Key questions if you have strong Activist preferences

- Will I be likely to learn something new, i.e. that I didn't know/couldn't do before?

- Will there be a wide variety of different activities?
  (I don't want to sit and listen for more than an hour at a stretch!)

- Will it be OK to have a go/let my hair down/make mistakes?

- Will I encounter tough problems and challenges?

- Will there be other like-minded people to mix with/have fun with?

- Will there be lots to do/lots of opportunities to participate?

If you have a preference for the **Reflector** style:

you will learn most easily from activities where

- you are allowed or encouraged to watch/think/chew over activities
- you are able to stand back from events and listen/observe, e.g. take a back seat in a group activity, watch a film or video
- you are allowed to think before acting, e.g. time to prepare, a chance to read background information in advance
- you can carry out some painstaking research, e.g. investigate, gather information, probe to get to the bottom of things
- you have the opportunity to think about what has happened, what you have learned
- you are asked to produce carefully considered analyses and reports
- you can reach a decision in your own time without pressure and tight deadlines.

you will find it more difficult to learn from activities where

- you are 'forced' into the limelight, e.g. to act as leader, to role-play in front of onlookers
- you are involved in situations that require action without planning
- you are pitched into doing something without warning, e.g. to produce an instant reaction, to produce a spontaneous idea
- you are given insufficient information on which to base a conclusion
- you are given cut and dried instructions of how things should be done
- you are worried by time pressures or rushed from one activity to another
- you are not given time to do a thorough job.

Key questions if you have strong Reflector preferences

- Will I be given adequate time to consider, assimilate and prepare?

- Will there be opportunities/facilities to gather relevant information?

- Will there be opportunities to listen to other people's points of view? (Preferably a wide cross-section of people with a variety of views.)

- Will I have adequate time to prepare and not be under pressure to be slapdash or to think on my feet?

- Will there be useful opportunities to watch other people in action?

If you have a preference for the **Theorist** style:

you will learn most easily from activities where

- you have time to be methodical and to explore the associations and inter-relationships between ideas, events and situations
- you have the chance to question and probe the basic methodology, assumptions or logic behind something, e.g. by taking part in a question and answer session, by checking a newspaper for inconsistencies
- you are intellectually stretched, e.g. by analysing a complex situation, being tested in a tutorial session, by working with people who ask searching questions
- you are in structured situations with a clear purpose
- you can listen to, or read about, ideas and concepts that emphasise rationality or logic and are well argued/watertight
- you are offered interesting ideas and concepts, even though they may not be immediately relevant
- you are required to understand and participate in complex situations.

you will find it more difficult to learn from activities where

- you are required to do something without enough background information or an apparent purpose
- you have to participate in situations emphasising emotions and feelings
- you are involved in unstructured activities where uncertainty is high
- you are asked to act, or decide, without proper guidelines
- you are faced with a hotchpotch of alternative/contradictory techniques/ methods
- you doubt that the subject matter is methodologically sound, e.g. where questionnaires haven't been validated, where there aren't any statistics to support the argument
- you find the subject matter banal, shallow or gimmicky
- you feel yourself out of tune with other participants, e.g. when with lots of Activists or people of lower intellectual calibre.

Key questions if you have strong Theorist preferences

- Will there be lots of opportunities to ask questions?
- Will there be clear objectives and a plan/structure to achieve them?
- Will I encounter complex ideas and concepts that are likely to stretch me?
- Will the approaches used and concepts explored be 'respectable', i.e. sound and valid?
- Will I be with people of similar calibre to myself?
- Will this experience give me the chance to develop a general view or model?

If you have a preference for the **Pragmatist** style:

you will learn most easily from activities where

- there is an obvious link between the subject matter and a current problem or opportunity at work
- you are shown techniques for doing things with obvious practical advantages, e.g. how to save time, how to make a good first impression, how to deal with awkward people
- you have the chance to try out and practise techniques with coaching from someone you trust, who is successful and can do the techniques themselves
- you have the opportunity to learn from a demonstration by someone with a proven track record or a film showing how it is done
- you are shown techniques that apply to what you are trying to achieve
- you are given immediate opportunities to implement what you have learned
- you can concentrate on practical issues, e.g. by drawing up action plans with an obvious end product, suggesting short cuts, giving tips.

you will find it more difficult to learn from activities where

- the learning is not related to an immediate need you recognise/see or an immediate relevance/practical benefit
- organisers of the learning or the event itself seem distanced from reality, i.e. 'ivory towered', all theory and general principles, pure 'chalk and talk'
- there is no practice or clear guidelines on how to do it
- you feel that people are going round in circles and not getting anywhere fast enough
- there are political, managerial or personal obstacles to implementation
- you can't see sufficient reward from the learning activity.

Key questions if you have strong Pragmatist preferences

- Will there be ample opportunities to practise and experiment?
- Will there be lots of practical tips and techniques?
- Will I be addressing *real* problems and will it result in action plans to tackle some of my current problems?
- Will I be exposed to experts who know how to/can do it themselves?
- Will this really improve my immediate performance?

SECTION 9

Suggestions to strengthen an under-utilised style

This section is designed to help you develop and strengthen learning styles that you are currently under-utilising. There is a suggestion for action for every item in the questionnaire. For convenience, they are grouped by style so you will find, for example, all the suggestions to strengthen the activist style together, then the suggestions for reflector and so on.

Do not necessarily expect ready-made suggestions that you can immediately implement. If this happens it is a bonus. It is much more likely that a suggestion will provide you with the germ of an idea that you will need to develop into something that is feasible in your specific circumstances. Advice on how to firm up realistic action plans is given in section 11.

Clearly, with 40 suggestions on offer you will need to be ruthlessly selective. Look first at the suggestions to strengthen a style where you scored yourself relatively low. Then, within that factor, focus on items you crossed. Even then it is wise to limit yourself to a maximum of three simultaneous actions. More than this and you will tend to lose the plot.

Activist

The statement in **bold** is followed by the suggestion for action.

1   I quite like taking risks.

Risks fall into two categories: silly ones and calculated ones. To become less risk-averse, try experimenting with some calculated risks which, if they don't work out, will not have unacceptable consequences either for you or anyone else.

5   I often do things just because I feel like it, rather than thinking about them first.

No matter how much you pride yourself on being rational and logical, in the last analysis your decisions and actions are based on what feels right. So, let your hair down, back a hunch and occasionally do something for the sheer hell of it! This will help you learn to trust your feelings more.

9   I actively look for new things to do.

If you tend to be wary of new things you haven't tried before, set yourself a target to do, say, one new thing each week. It does not have to be particularly dramatic or risky; it could just be a change to your work routine or taking a different route to work. *Anything* to keep you open to newness and experimentation.

13   I like the challenge of trying out different ways of doing things.

It is easy to become set in your ways and resistant to different ways of doing things. Comfort zones are popular precisely because they are so comfortable! Become an experimenter. Set yourself the challenge of tackling something you do routinely in a different way. It will get you into experimental mode and make routine tasks much more exciting.

17   I prefer to jump in and do things as they come along rather than plan things out beforehand.

Increase your tolerance for spontaneity by choosing to react to events rather than adhering to a pre-set plan. There is a time to be proactive and a time to be reactive. Free up some time each day to react to events on a purely spontaneous basis.

21   In discussions, I usually come up with lots of spontaneous ideas.

In discussions/meetings, give yourself permission to express your ideas without censoring them. This will help your ideas to be more spontaneous and creative. You can always signal what you are up to by saying 'I'm just thinking aloud here' or 'This might sound a bit wild but how about...?'

Activist contd.

25 **Usually I talk more than I listen.**

Being a good listener is admirable but there are occasions when it pays to do the talking. Earmark times when it is appropriate for you to have most of the say, and make notes that you can use as prompts and go for it! At the very least set a 50/50 target - half the time talking, the other half listening.

29 **I find rules and procedures take the fun out of things.**

Try treating rules and procedures as general guidelines rather than rigid constraints that must be adhered to 'come what may'. Have fun seeing how far you can go within the rules, challenging rules and procedures that have passed their sell-by date.

33 **I'm usually the 'life and soul' of the party.**

Literally being the 'life and soul' of the party may be stretching it a bit, but you could at least practise being more outgoing. At parties or large gatherings, set yourself the objective of initiating cheerful conversations with a set number of strangers. Progressively push up your target as you get into the swing of things.

37 **I enjoy the excitement of a crisis situation.**

A crisis, by definition, is something short-lived and rather chaotic that demands immediate attention. Clearly, there is no point in creating crises just to practise enjoying them more! When they do occur, however, use them to increase your tolerance for chaos and uncertainty and to learn to relish the drama and excitement while it lasts.

Reflector

The statement in **bold** is followed by the suggestion for action.

2   **Before taking part in a discussion or meeting, I like to read the appropriate papers and prepare carefully.**

If you tend to skimp the preparation for meetings, make it a rule that, before all meetings where an agenda has been issued in advance, you will spend at least fifteen minutes collecting your thoughts and reading supporting papers. Use these more formal meetings as the spur to devoting more time to preparation.

6   **I make decisions only after weighing up the pros and cons of different possibilities.**

Cut and dried 'right' decisions are rare. More usually there are a number of possibilities to consider when deciding the best way forward. If you tend to be an impatient decision maker, force yourself to slow down. Identify, say, three different possibilities to weigh up and list the advantages and disadvantages of each. The quality of your decisions should improve - and so will your attention to detail.

10   **I prefer to establish the facts and think things through before reaching a conclusion.**

If you tend to jump to conclusions with limited information, try consciously to postpone reaching a conclusion and, instead, put your energy into collecting some relevant facts. Then base your conclusion on the facts. This will increase your tolerance for ambiguity, i.e. not knowing what the answer is while you gather facts, and your respect for data collection.

14   **I prefer to have as many bits of information about a subject as possible. The more I have to sift through the better.**

Become an information 'junkie' by gathering bits and pieces of information on a topic or subject area. Imagine you are conducting the equivalent of a painstaking police investigation where many fragments of information, some apparently unrelated, need to be pieced together to build up a comprehensive picture.

18   **I prefer to base decisions on hard evidence and not to trust a hunch or intuition.**

Try collecting some hard evidence to reduce the guesswork in your decision making. Inevitably, there will still be plenty of unknowns where you'll need your intuition, but a mix of facts and intuition will stand you in better stead than one without the other.

Reflector contd.

22   **I prefer to look at a problem from as many different angles as I can before starting to solve it.**

Problems are open to differing interpretations and are often in the eye of the beholder. Time spent on different descriptions of the problem will often open up fresh, and more promising, interpretations. So, try assuming that the initial description of the problem is just the first of, say, three of four different ways of looking at it. Actively consider alternative interpretations - even if, having done so, you go with your original one.

26   **If I have to write a report or a formal letter, I prefer to have several rough drafts before settling on the final version.**

If you are the sort of person who dashes off a piece of writing without giving it a second glance, force yourself to treat it like a draft. Put it aside, 'sleep on it' and return to it a day or so later with the aim of improving it. This will help you reflect on your work. You will be amazed how often doing so will help you make significant improvements.

30   **I like to consider many options before I make up my mind.**

Get into the habit of thinking of, say, six possible options before making up your mind about a course of action. This will open up your mind to a range of possibilities and wean you off the tendency to take on the first expedient thing that occurs to you.

34   **I like to think through the consequences before taking action.**

Cut the tendency to take action on 'a suck it and see' basis with little or no regard for the consequences. Decide on an action and then, before implementing it, identify some consequences by asking 'what if?' questions. Think hard about each consequence before settling on the action that is most likely to lead to a favourable outcome.

38   **I usually do more listening than talking.**

Practise listening hard with your undivided attention. Taking copious notes - even writing down some things verbatim - helps to get you focused on listening, not contributing. It also helps to imagine you are going to be called upon to give a detailed summary of what you have heard! Deep listening is definitely a skill worth learning.

Theorist

The statement in **bold** is followed by the suggestion for action.

3   **I like to be absolutely correct about things.**

Step up your attention to detail. Select some pieces of work where correctness definitely matters and go through them carefully dotting the i's and crossing the t's. Experimenting with a zero-tolerance-for-errors policy, in selected cases, will help you increase the value you place on things being correct.

7   **I prefer to solve problems using a systematic approach that reduces guesswork and uncertainty.**

Even the most systematic approach to problem solving will leave you with some unknowns and uncertainties. Reduce the guesswork by adopting a logical step-by-step methodology where the problem is defined carefully and criteria are used to evaluate potential solutions.

11   **I like to check things out for myself rather than take them for granted.**

There is a time to check and a time to take things on trust. Work out when it would be foolhardy not to check, i.e. when the consequences of an error are unacceptable. Remember the maxim 'people do what's checked, not what you expect'. This should help to bolster your resolve to do more checking.

15   **I am quite keen on sticking to fixed routines, following procedures and keeping to timetables.**

Try subjecting yourself to a pre-planned routine or procedure that, in your heart of hearts, you know would improve your self-discipline. You could experiment, for example, with a time management routine or with a strict diet/exercise regime. Once you have decided upon a routine, the challenge is to stick to it, come what may.

19   **I like to fit things into some sort of pattern, framework or model.**

Look for themes and patterns that link disparate ideas, theories and approaches. Try taking some raw data and sorting it into categories. Or take two different ideas and try putting them together in a 2x2 table. The whole idea is to practise integrating things to form a coherent model or framework.

Theorist contd.

23   **I prefer to evaluate the soundness of my ideas before sharing them.**

If you are the sort of person who is happy to 'brainstorm' ideas, with no preparation or deep thought, try slowing down and listing your ideas. Then assume that each idea in turn is going to be scrutinised. Prepare to defend each idea and only retain those that you can back up with a convincing rationale. This will give you practice in evaluating the soundness of your ideas.

27   **I am rather fussy about how I do things – a bit of a perfectionist.**

Take a piece of work you have done and go back over it with a fine tooth comb. Correct any errors, however small, and set yourself the objective of making at least three improvements. This may seem obtuse, but it is deliberately designed to get you to 'fuss' over details and become more of a perfectionist.

31   **I believe that careful, logical thinking is the key to success.**

Set aside some time each day as thinking time. Fifteen to twenty minutes should suffice. Have a list of things to think about rather than spending valuable time wondering what to think about! You could think about your longer-term strategy, your key deliverables for next week, how to improve a product or service so that it delights more customers, how to cut costs and so on. Then think about whether thinking more has helped you to be more successful.

35   **I like to understand the assumptions, principles and rationale upon which things are based.**

Ask questions to surface the assumptions upon which decisions, strategies and actions are based. Question people about their basic beliefs and the philosophy that underpins their life and work. The whole idea is to practise getting behind the façade, to develop a deeper understanding of the reasons why things are as they are.

39   **I like meetings and discussions to be structured and orderly.**

Clarify the purpose of meetings and discussions in which you are involved. Insist on a structure and sequence of events that will maximise the probability of achieving the stated purpose. Press for the proceedings to be orderly - perhaps by volunteering to chair discussions yourself. Placing emphasis on structure and order will help you value these things more highly.

Pragmatist

The statement in **bold** is followed by the suggestion for action.

4   **I like practical, tried and tested techniques.**

Become a technique collector, by showing an interest in practical methods that have been tried and tested. Ask your colleagues for hints and tips about how they do things. Read materials with a 'how to' practical bent.

8   **What matters most is whether something works in practice.**

Be a realist and put practical considerations above all else. Remember the saying 'there is nothing so practical as a good theory'. Test out ideas to see which are fit for purpose and work best in your circumstances.

12   **When I hear about a new idea or technique, I immediately start working out how to apply it to my situation/problems.**

When you come across a new idea or technique, think about how you could apply it beneficially to your work. The toughest cases will be with methods and techniques that come from unrelated fields. However, it is still worth exploring how they might be adapted to suit your circumstances.

16   **In discussions, I like to get straight to the point.**

Before taking part in discussions, set yourself a realistic objective and allow this to guide your behaviour. Stay focused on whatever it is you wish to achieve, minimising preliminaries and deviations. Practise being business-like in your resolve to reach your objective, but not to the extent of being brusque or obstinate.

20   **I tend to judge people's ideas on their practical merits.**

Ideas come in different shapes and sizes. Some are wild, some are esoteric, some are elegant and some are practical. Practise using the latter as your yardstick for judging the usefulness of an idea. Keep checking ideas to assess how they are likely to work out in practice. Make practicality your main criteria for acceptance.

24   **In meetings and discussions, I put forward ideas that I know are down-to-earth and realistic.**

In meetings and discussions concentrate on generating ideas that are down-to-earth and realistic. Keep doing reality checks on your ideas by assessing them against a backcloth of what is feasible given your resources (time, people, equipment, money etc.) and general circumstances. If the idea doesn't measure up, abandon it for something more practical or modify it to make it feasible.

Pragmatist contd.

28   I find that I can often work out more practical ways of doing things.
When you acquire a method, approach or technique from another source, see if you can streamline it, or find shortcuts to make it more user-friendly. Get into the habit of experimenting with adaptations. It is often possible to amalgamate steps, or modify the sequence, to finish up with something more practical.

32   I prefer ideas with an obvious relevance to my life and work.
Make relevance your first priority. Go for things where you can quickly see the possibility of a promising pay-off. This means putting a premium on things that are relevant but will not necessarily result in quick fixes.

36   In my opinion, it doesn't matter how you do something, as long as it works.
Keep trying things to see how they work out in practice. There is no substitute for a trial run or a pilot. The only way to discover whether things work is to test them. So, become an experimenter and find out from first-hand experience what works and what doesn't.

40   I do whatever I need to, to get the job done.
Providing it is ethical, concentrate on doing whatever is expedient to get the job done. Have a clear end in view and go for it with single-minded resolution.

SECTION 10

Getting help and support from others

Other people, such as your manager, immediate colleagues or mentor (if you have one), can be especially helpful when:

- you have completed and scored your questionnaire and want to check whether other people have useful views on your approach to learning

- you want to make decisions about the kind of learning activities you should seek and get feedback on how you are using learning opportunities

- you want help/support with strengthening an under-utilised learning style.

Checking your score

Obviously the checking process is best done by someone who both knows you well and understands learning styles, but the latter is not essential. The most detailed and useful approach is to ask someone to do the questionnaire about you. If there are substantial differences in your perceptions, as shown in the total scores, then it is worth going over the individual questions to check the differences in detail and the reasons for them.

Your immediate manager may be best equipped to do this – and it may lead to extra benefits in developing your learning interactions. However, you may be more comfortable asking a colleague to share their perceptions with you. You could ask a domestic partner, but there may well be some major differences in your behaviour at home as opposed to your behaviour whilst at work!

Deciding on learning activities

Your questionnaire results can be used to help you choose which learning activities to undertake. Your manager or training adviser could assist you with this in two ways. They could help to check that any association you make between your style and an activity is accurate; are you right to assume that a particular course would give you insufficient scope as, say, a strong Reflector? Secondly, they could help to point you in the direction of opportunities that make use of your strengths or assist you in overcoming some weaknesses. You can then set out what you will do – perhaps in a personal development plan.

As with many things in life, the distance between planning to do something and actually achieving it can be substantial.

The role of the helper here can be to encourage you to act, to discuss opportunities and to help you by giving you feedback. You should be selective and ask them to watch for particular things. They should not be asked, "How well do you think I am learning?". Ask instead, "What did you think about my response to that situation? Did I...?".

Strengthening a style

Your manager and/or colleagues can be supportive as you struggle to increase the use of an underdeveloped learning style. In addition to providing you with feedback, they could help more practically by encouraging you to experiment. For example, if you wanted to practise being more of an Activist, they could allow you to take the lead in a brainstorming session or they could support your attempts to have, say, ten minutes per day as ring-fenced reflection time.

Clearly, if this sort of help is to be forthcoming, you will need to be open about the learning style you are seeking to enhance. The best of all possible worlds is if you have a colleague or colleagues who are also intent on expanding their repertoire of learning styles. This can lead to a mutually supportive atmosphere that everyone can enjoy and learn from.

Understanding the sort of help you are likely to get/not get from your manager

Managers have learning style preferences too! The help and support they are likely to provide will vary depending on their preferences. Here are lists to help you appreciate the sort of help you can expect.

The Activist manager

Activist managers will tend to help by:

- Generating (unconsciously) opportunities for others to observe and reflect on what they do
- Taking an optimistic and positive view of what is involved in a new situation
- Giving a positive and encouraging lead (at least initially, in the short term) and active learning opportunities
- Following through with action to provide learning experiences if they have been convinced of their value
- Responding spontaneously to opportunities as they arise.

Activist managers will be less likely to provide help through:

- Providing planned learning experiences
- Giving support to learning as a planned, structured activity
- Assessing and using learning experiences that are different to those through which they have learned
- Discussing learning opportunities beforehand and reviewing them afterwards

- Standing back and allowing others to participate or take action
- Giving different learning experiences to employees with different learning styles.

The Reflector manager

Reflector managers will tend to help by:

- Suggesting activities that can be observed
- Recommending how observation can be carried out
- Identifying ways in which an event or a problem can be analysed
- Discussing what may happen and reviewing what has happened
- Providing data or feedback in a controlled learning environment
- Advising how to prepare carefully for a management activity
- Not taking a dominant role in meetings with employees
- Emphasising the importance of collecting data before taking action
- Giving a controlled response to requests for help.

Reflector managers will be less likely to provide help through:

- Suggesting ad hoc, immediate learning opportunities
- Showing how to take advantage spontaneously of unplanned learning activities
- Providing unexpected or slightly risky learning situations, e.g. sudden delegation of a task
- Giving immediate answers to unexpected requests for direct help
- Providing a large-scale view of philosophy, concept, system or policy
- Providing a strong personal model of anything except Reflector behaviour.

The Theorist manager

Theorist managers will tend to help by:

- Showing interest in any intellectually respectable idea
- Helping people to describe underlying causes, to explain the systems or concepts involved in any activity
- Demonstrating the intellectual validity of an answer or process
- Showing how to strengthen or demolish a case by the use of logic
- Bringing out complexities
- Aiming for clarity of structure or purpose
- Articulating theories, e.g. Open Systems Theory, or Theory X and Theory Y
- Generalising reasons why something works or does not work
- Setting high standards for quality of data.

Theorist managers will be less likely to provide help through:

- Showing when to accept the obvious
- Helping others to understand emotions and feelings in specific circumstances
- Making use of data or occasions that conflict with their theories
- Developing others who are different in intellectual level or style, e.g. if theories clash with their own
- Showing how to use information that they regard as trivial, irrelevant, or not intellectually respectable
- Drawing up specific action plans.

The Pragmatist manager

Pragmatist managers will tend to help by:

- Showing responsiveness to new ideas and techniques
- Demonstrating interest in specific action plans
- Pressing for relevant learning programmes with clear payoff
- Being open to new situations
- Showing a belief in the possibility of improvement
- Following the party line, e.g. on appraisals or releasing people for courses
- Following specific suggestions on how to improve learning.

Pragmatist managers will be less likely to provide help through:

- Being responsive to ideas or techniques not immediately relevant to a current problem
- Showing interest in concepts or theories
- Encouraging action relevant to the longer term
- Encouraging ideas or learning programmes that they regard as unproved or off-base
- Pushing for action that apparently is not valued by the culture or system
- Using learning opportunities that they see as unrelated to real life, e.g. seminars by "people who don't understand our industry/organisation/problems".

Clearly, if managers know what kinds of learning activities they are not likely to provide themselves, they may be (and of course, in terms of responsibility, ought to be) at least responsive to suggestions outside their own style. The best managers will actively seek to fill in the gaps by using other people and resources.

SECTION 11

Advice on planning actions and keeping a Learning Log

If you are to improve it is vital that you decide to do something *at once*. The perils are that you will feel:

- overwhelmed by the number and variety of things you could do

- that to do just one or two things would be futile: an 'all or nothing' philosophy

- that the time isn't right and that it would be better to wait for more favourable conditions.

All these and any more you can dream up seem like plausible excuses for procrastination. But if you allow yourself to succumb, the chances are that you will never get around to doing anything.

Implementation is easy once you have decided precisely what you want to do. The object of this short section is to make it as likely as possible that you will have an action plan you can implement quickly.

It is of the utmost importance that you limit the number of simultaneous actions to an absolute maximum of three. If you take on more, the chances are you will find you have been over-ambitious. It is far easier to focus on limited incremental improvement. So be patient and tackle your development in manageable steps. Once you have been successful with your first tranche of actions, you can always come back for more by consulting additional thought-starters.

Your actions can either be 'bunched' by concentrating on one factor or they can be 'spread' across different factors.

In order to be sufficiently robust, all your action plans should meet the following quality standards:

- they should be feasible

- they should be immediate

- they should be selective/focused

- they should be specific.

You also need to consider whether:

- you need help to implement your plan (and if so, who can provide it)

- to go public about your plan or 'just do it'.

Personal Development Plan

What I am going to do

Why I am going to do this

How I am going to do this

When I am going to do this

When I will review the results/how I will know I was successful

Keeping a Learning Log

A learning log is a discipline to help you to review an experience from which you wish to learn.

Specifically, the learning log is designed to help you to:

- review the experience (stage 2 of the learning cycle)

- reach conclusions (stage 3 of the learning cycle)

- plan what to do better/differently (stage 4 of the learning cycle).

Keeping a log also helps to 'force' you (if that is what it takes) to search out and take learning opportunities, since the discipline of making log entries puts a certain amount of pressure on you to have something to enter!

Each time you use your learning log follow this procedure:

1   Start by thinking back over an experience and selecting a part of it to focus on in your log. You might choose something that was significant or important to you. On the other hand, you could choose something that struck you as routine or even mundane. Whatever you choose to focus on, the log invites you to be selective. You don't need to write at length about *everything* that happened.

2   Write a detailed account of what happened during the period or activity you have chosen to focus on. Don't at this stage put any effort into deciding what you have learned – just concentrate on describing what actually happened.

3   List the conclusions you have reached as a result of pondering the experience. These are, in effect, your learning points. Don't limit the number and don't worry about the practicality of the points you list. They are likely to be a mixture of things you 'knew' before as well as new insights.

4   Finally, decide which learning points you want to implement in the future and work out an action plan that covers:

   -    what you are going to do

   -    when you are going to do it.

Spell out your action plan as precisely as possible so that it is realistic and you are clear how to implement it.

It is not necessary to complete all these steps in one go. You could, for example, write a description of what happened while it is fresh in your mind and at some later stage, after time for reflection, record your conclusions and plan. Even the conclusions and the plan could be recorded at different times. The important thing, however, is eventually to have filled in all three boxes, albeit not in one sitting, thus ensuring that you complete all the stages in the learning cycle.

Here is a simple format for a learning log. If you wish you could incorporate a similar process in your diary or personal organiser.

You can purchase the Learning Log booklet from Peter Honey Publications at the address given at the beginning of this booklet.

Learning Log

My description of what happened

My conclusions/'lessons learned'

My plan to do something better/different

APPENDIX

Questions and answers about Learning Styles and the 40-item version of the Questionnaire

These are some of the questions people most often ask about learning styles and the shortened version of the Learning Styles Questionnaire.

Are there only four learning styles?

Four learning styles offer three worthwhile and practical advantages:

- they are easy to remember

- they reinforce the stages people need to go through in order to be balanced learners

- they are widely understood, accepted and used by learners.

The four styles are a convenient way of describing differences in learning preferences and, of course, they map onto the stages on each loop of the continuous learning cycle. Some researchers have suggested that there are only two learning styles or orientations: doing and thinking. The doing orientation tends to overlap with a combination of Activist and Pragmatist. The thinking orientation overlaps with Reflector and Theorist.

Aren't labels misleading/stereotyping?

Like any categorisation they are a convenient oversimplification. The styles have to be called something; the labels Activist, Reflector, Theorist and Pragmatist are a convenient shorthand. The labels are only a starting point for discussion on how you learn. The most dangerous tendency to guard against is using a label as an excuse not to change: "I'm an Activist so you can't expect me to attend to any details".

Why was the 40-item version of the questionnaire created?

There were two interrelated reasons.

Firstly, following the success of the 80-item version, there was a request for a cut-down version of the questionnaire to be produced for an audience of young people engaged in government-sponsored youth employment programmes. This led to a version of the questionnaire where the number of items was halved and the wording of some items was simplified (to make them less managerial). However, at the time this version of the questionnaire, designed to meet a specific one-off need, was not offered to a wider audience.

Secondly, in 2000 we decided to produce an online version of the LSQ as part of our *Learning Series.* We shortened the questionnaire so that it was more appropriate to the technology and similar in length to the other questionnaires that make up the *Series.*

Since the shortened version has proved popular with some users, we have now decided to complement the online version by also offering it as a booklet.

How did you decide which items to include in the 40-item version?

We used two criteria.

1 We excluded items in the original 80-item version that failed to discriminate sufficiently between people with different preferences, i.e. items that were 'ticked' by at least 80% of a large sample of respondents. This indicated 27 questionnaire items that could be deleted.

2 We then examined the remaining 53 items and removed those that tended to overlap.

Does this mean that the wording of the items in the shortened questionnaire is identical to their equivalents in the 80-item version?

No. We took the opportunity to improve the wording of some items. 40% of the statements in the 40-item version are identical to their 80-item equivalents and 60% have been reworded. Typically, the reworked statements are clearer, less ambiguous and more succinct than the originals. Examples are:

Original wording	New wording
I often act without considering the possible consequences.	I quite like taking risks.
I tend to be attracted to techniques such as network analysis, flow charts, branching programmes, contingency planning, etc.	I like practical, tried and tested techniques.
I think that decisions based on a thorough analysis of all the information are sounder than those based on intuition.	I prefer to base decisions on hard evidence rather than hunches or intuition.
I am keen on self-discipline such as watching my diet, taking regular exercise, sticking to a fixed routine, etc.	I am quite keen on sticking to fixed routines, following procedures and keeping to timetables.

How did you test the reliability and validity of the 40-item LSQ?

We asked for volunteers to complete both versions of the questionnaire so that we could compare the two sets of results. 203 people volunteered to help - predominately trainers, development specialists, consultants and people from the HR function, i.e. not a random cross-section of the general population. A comparison of the mean scores for each learning style show that the volunteers tended to have stronger Activist and lower Reflector/Theorist preferences than the general population. This confirms the trend we discovered for trainers when we first established norms for the 80-item questionnaire.

To what extent does the shortened questionnaire give the same results as the longer 80-item LSQ?

The correlations (Pearson's product-moment coefficient of correlation) between responses to the 40-item questionnaire and to the equivalent items in the 80-item version were as follows:

Activist	0.81
Reflector	0.78
Theorist	0.72
Pragmatist	0.79

Not unexpectedly, these correlations become even stronger when you compare the way people responded to the items that were identical in both versions of the questionnaire:

Activist	0.90
Reflector	0.86
Theorist	0.81
Pragmatist	0.89

You might wonder why responses to identical items show any variances at all! Many factors could influence this such as the elapsed time between completing the two different versions of the questionnaire (we had no control over this with our volunteer group). Also, since the items appear in a different sequence in the two versions of the questionnaire, the positioning of identically-worded statements within each questionnaire could be another variable that, in some subtle way, influences the way people react.

It is worth noting that where the scores for the two versions of the questionnaire did not exactly match, the differences usually occurred because borderline scores were juxtaposed. So, for example, a score at the top of the moderate band on one questionnaire might finish up in the bottom of the strong band on the other or a score at the top of the low band might have crept up so that it finished as a low moderate. 'Near misses' such as these accounted for:

90% of the Activist differences

86% of the Reflector differences

80% of the Theorist differences

74% of the Pragmatist differences

What other trends emerged from the analysis of the 40-item version of the questionnaire?

In addition to calculating the correlations, we analysed a number of other factors.

Dominant styles

An assumption lurking behind learning style preferences is that someone with four more or less equally balanced preferences would be better equipped to complete all the stages in the learning cycle (see Section 2) than someone with, say, just one dominant preference.

We therefore looked at the pattern of 'very strong' and 'strong' preferences amongst our group of 203 volunteers. For the purposes of this study, 'strong' is defined as the top 30% of scores, i.e. the top 10% (very strong) and the next 20% (strong) scores have been combined. The findings were:

80-item version		**40-item version**	
One strong preference	33%	One strong preference	39%
Two strong preferences	22%	Two strong preferences	21%
Three strong preferences	7%	Three strong preferences	4%
Four strong preferences	0%	Four strong preferences	0%
No strong preferences	38%	No strong preferences	36%

As you can see, these results show that no one in the volunteer group had four strong preferences. This is not unusual and compares with 2% who had four strong preferences when responses to the 80-item questionnaire were first analysed back in 1982. The results, then and now, confirm our proposition that, if people are to become more flexible, better-rounded learners, they need to expand their repertoire (see Section 9).

The 'no strong preference' groups include people who had a mixture of moderate and low preferences. To complete the picture, here is a breakdown of the moderate preferences, i.e. where the scores fell into the middle 40% band.

80-item version		**40-item version**	
One moderate preference	36%	One moderate preference	41%
Two moderate preferences	41%	Two moderate preferences	39%
Three moderate preferences	18%	Three moderate preferences	16%
Four moderate preferences	5%	Four moderate preferences	4%
No moderate preferences	0%	No moderate preferences	0%

Popular combinations

We looked at people's first and second preferences to see what combinations of learning style preferences were most prevalent. The findings were:

First and second preference 'combinations'	Percentage of volunteer group
Activist/Pragmatist	32%
Reflector/Theorist	24%
Reflector/Pragmatist	19%
Activist/Reflector	10.4%
Theorist/Pragmatist	9.9%
Activist/Theorist	3.9%

Can learning style preferences change?

Yes, learning styles, just like any other learned characteristics, are modifiable either at will or by a change of circumstances. Many people have successfully strengthened an underdeveloped style and thus become a more rounded learner. Alternatively, when people change jobs and/or organisations, the altered influences have an effect on learning styles. Suppose, for example, you moved from a 'quick fix' culture to an organisation that by the nature of its work was more reflective. The decrease in the speed of working, and the emphasis placed on the painstaking collection and analysis of data, would be likely to increase your Reflector/Theorist behaviour and, over time, to affect your overall preferences. It may well be that your 'first love' preferences for Pragmatist/Activist would still predominate, but being forced to use Reflector/Theorist would undoubtedly strengthen their presence in your repertoire.

Why do the questionnaire items probe general behavioural tendencies and not learning?

Since most people have never consciously considered how they learn, it is not helpful to ask questions that directly enquire into this. If you ask people how they learn prior to introducing them to the continuous learning cycle, they will simply say they 'just do' and are often incapable of articulating the process they go through. It is more useful, therefore, to ask you questions you can answer that are indirectly indicative of your preferred learning styles. To do so is certainly more helpful (there seems little point in asking you questions you can't answer!) and enjoys greater face validity. The items in the questionnaire also admirably illustrate how learning style preferences underpin, and are associated with, everyday behavioural tendencies. This helps demonstrate the fundamental importance of learning styles.

How accurate are self-perceptions?

The way you view yourself is likely to be confirmed by people who know you well in a work context or have worked closely with you on, say, a course. (Views of a domestic partner may differ, as some of us behave differently at home!)

Sometimes a third-party observer of someone's outward behaviour may conclude that the person had, say, Activist preferences. This is because people sometimes behave one way whilst feeling/thinking another way. Someone with Reflector preferences may, for example, behave like an Activist because that is expected of them and/or there is pressure to do so. Other people inevitably have to base their perceptions on the behaviour they observe. This may mislead them into concluding that behaviour is inevitably indicative of an underlying preference. When it comes to likes and dislikes, each individual is best qualified to answer.

However, it is of course possible that self-perceptions are inaccurate. The answers are easy to fake if someone is determined to give a misleading impression. To do so would spoil the purpose of the questionnaire - which is to aid self-awareness and development.

Why does the questionnaire only allow a binary choice, tick or cross?

To keep it simple. In the original research we tested a version of the questionnaire with a range of answers such as very frequently – frequently – sometimes – infrequently – never. It rendered the same preferences as the simpler version. We therefore decided to keep it simple and not to complicate the questionnaire unnecessarily. As a consequence, some people feel uncomfortable with being forced to respond one way or the other but they are usually reassured when they understand that the questionnaire is designed to reveal four general tendencies and not a detailed analysis of their whole personality.

Must all the questionnaire items be answered?

Yes, because if some items are left blank they might all fall within one learning style and therefore lead to an underestimate of your preference for that style.

What if you don't believe your results?

We suggest you try the following:

1 Check that you still accept each tick/cross.

2 Re-examine items that were marginal to see if you had a tendency to cross them. If so, and only in those cases that were marginal, rescore your questionnaire assuming that the marginal crosses are ticks. This adjustment may give you a more believable result. You might also want to try the next suggestion.

3 Collect feedback from other people's observations of you to see to what extent their perceptions match the questionnaire results. In our experience when this has been done, the feedback tends to confirm the preferences indicated by the scores.

Other Booklets from Peter Honey Publications

The Learning Styles Questionnaire (80-item version) – Peter Honey and Alan Mumford

We all have preferred ways of learning and learn better from some activities than others. This comprehensive booklet provides individuals with all the tools they need to identify their preferred learning style(s), to select learning opportunities that suit stronger styles and to develop weaker ones.

The Learning Styles Helper's Guide – Peter Honey and Alan Mumford

This booklet provides comprehensive guidance for all helpers of learning and is the ideal companion to *The Learning Styles Questionnaire*. It explores activities that suit different learning styles and provides practical advice on using learning styles in conjunction with training programmes and personal development plans.

The Trainer Styles Questionnaire – Peter Honey

Trainers and developers have learning style preferences too! But, it is one thing to think of your preferences as a learner and another to think of your preferences as a trainer. The Trainer Styles Questionnaire featured in this booklet is a useful way of exploring the issues from a trainer's perspective. Written in the same style as The Learning Styles Questionnaire booklets it contains helpful insights we hope will contribute significantly to your continuing professional development as a trainer.

Continuous Personal Development – Peter Honey

This booklet has two aims; to encourage people to take responsibility for their own development and to show them how to make the whole process really useful. As the name implies, this booklet goes beyond the usual 'professional' development and places the accent on taking personal initiatives through self-development. The benefits of this are explained and there are ample spaces for people to produce personal development plans and learning logs.

How to become a more effective learner – Peter Honey

Everyone should treat learning as a skill that, like any other skill, is capable of improvement. Learning is learnable! Yet, sadly, adult learning is too often taken for granted and not continuously improved. This booklet contains the Learning Skills Questionnaire complete with score key and practical development suggestions.

Teams and Teamwork – Peter Honey

A booklet that can be used either by individuals to become more effective team members or by a group as a communal team-building process. Contains questionnaires that explore team roles and teamwork.

Valuing Diversity – Peter Honey

Everyone, everyday has to deal with diversity. The challenge is to turn the differences between people to advantage rather than suffering them or merely tolerating them. This booklet will show you how to use those differences as a powerful lever to get better results and greater harmony.

Licences to Print

Licences are available for some of our booklets, enabling you to print your own copies of the material from a file provided. Terms and conditions apply.

For more information on any of the above items please call the Peter Honey team on +44 (0)1628 633 946